MW00944355

For my daughter –
When leaving home, take these words
of wisdom. Because being kind is
always the best, and you are always
the best when being kind.
Love you to the moon and back,
Dad

HEY, _____

THANKS FOR NOT BEING
AN
A**HOLE!

FIRST EDITION 2019
HAHAHA! PARODY SERIES
VOL.1 NO.1
COLLECTOR'S EDITION

WRITTEN BY SHWA LAYTART
IG @GIGGLEPRODUCTIONS
GRAFFITI ILLUSTRATIONS BY SICKID
IG @SICKID1
BOOK DESIGN BY SUGAR

PUBLISHED BY AVANTPOP BOOKS
WWW.AVANTPOPBOOKS.COM
IG @AVANTPOPBOOKS

OH, THE A**HOLES YOU'LL MEET!

BY SHWA LAYTART
ILLUSTRATED BY SICKID

AVANTPOP BOOKS
& ART GALLERY

USA / EARTH

NOW I'M SURE YOU'LL BE
THE FIRST TO SAY
THAT EVEN I CAN BE AN A**HOLE
ON ANY GIVEN DAY.

LIVE YOUR LIFE WITH PATIENCE
AND AN OPEN MIND.
IT'S YOUR CHOICE EVERYDAY
TO BE AN A**HOLE OR KIND.

GO OUT AND HAVE FUN AND LIVE YOUR LIFE WELL. ENJOY THE JOURNEY AND THIS I CAN TELL...

SHWA LAYTART IS A WRITER, JOURNALIST, STORYTELLER AND WANNABE COMEDIAN. HIS GREATEST ACCOMPLISHMENT IS RAISING HIS DAUGHTER TO BE EVEN FUNNIER THAN HE IS. WHEN HE'S NOT WRITING HE'S COLLECTING BOOKS, ART, PLANTS AND ROCKS. IF YOU SEE HIM IN THE WILD, APPROACH SLOWLY AND OFFER HIM SOMETHING TO NUMB HIS NERVOUS SYSTEM.

SICKID IS A GRAFFITI ARTIST BASED IN LOS ANGELES. HIS WORK OFTEN SHOWS FIGURES PLACED IN SITUATIONS THAT ARE PERCEIVED AS TABOO OR NON-ACCEPTABLE TO THE MEANS OF CONSERVATIVE NORMS. THE CHARACTERS ARE DONE WITH A STYLE THAT REFLECTS ALTERNATIVE COMIC CULTURE AND EARLY JAPANESE ANIMATION AND HAVE A STRONG SENSE OF FESTIVITY AND HAPPINESS DUE TO THE REOCCURRING SATURATED COLOR PALETTE OFTEN USED. HIS PIECES SPREAD FROM LOS ANGELES TO INTERNATIONAL LENGTHS AND HIS PAINTINGS ARE NOW BEING FEATURED IN GALLERIES AS WELL AS THE STREETS.

CPSIA information can be obtained
at www.ICGtesting.com
Printed in the USA
BVHW022343201019
561613BV00002B/3/P